Maria SHCS

For Cirsten and Rolf

Philomel Books
an imprint of Penguin Random House LLC
New York, New York

Copyright © 1968 by Eric Carle.
Penguin supports copyright. Copyright fuels creativity, encourages diverse voices, promotes free
speech, and creates a vibrant culture. Thank you for buying an authorized edition of this book and
for complying with copyright laws by not reproducing, scanning, or distributing any part of it in
any form without permission. You are supporting writers and allowing Penguin to continue to
publish books for every reader.

Philomel Books is a registered trademark of Penguin Random House LLC.

Library of Congress Cataloging-in-Publication Data
Carle, Eric.
1, 2, 3 to the zoo / by Eric Carle
Summary: Each car on the train has one more zoo animal than the one before, from the first car
with one elephant to the last with ten birds.
Counting—Juvenile literature. [1. Counting 2. Zoo animals—Pictoral works] I. Title.
QA113.C37 1982 513/.2E 81-8609

Manufactured in China.
ISBN 9781101951279
Part of Boxed Set, ISBN 9781101951217
3 5 7 9 10 8 6 4 2

1, 2, 3
TO THE ZOO

a counting book by

ERIC CARLE

Philomel Books
an imprint of Penguin Random House, LLC.

1

2

3

5

1234567
345678
5678910
78910112
9101234